Cover illustration: The F-16/79 is being touted as an all-round fighter, with particular emphasis in the sales pitch on the aircraft's bomb-carrying ability. The aircraft shown here is loaded with six 500lb Mk. 82s along with a pair of 370-gallon external tanks. The Austrians expressed interest in the F-16/79 but decided not to buy for political reasons. On 25 June 1982, Peru became the first buyer for the F-16/79 (assuming Congressional approval), when it formally requested 24 single-seater and two trainers at approximately $14.5 million per aircraft, just over $1 million less than the standard F-16. (GD)

1. Loaded with three 370-gallon external tanks and a general purpose cargo pod (outboard), probably containing a change of clothing for the pilot, this 313th TFS Fighting Falcon takes off from Hahn AB, West Germany, on a long-range mission. Note the squadron insignia behind the position light on the intake. The 50th TFW at Hahn was the first USAF unit to receive MSIP I F-16s, December 1981. (GD)

America's Fighters of the 1980s: F16 and F18

ROBERT C. STERN

ARMS AND ARMOUR PRESS

London—Melbourne—Harrisburg, Pa.

Introduction

Warbirds 17: America's Fighters of the 1980s: The F-16 and F-18
Published in 1983 by
Arms and Armour Press, Lionel Leventhal Limited,
2-6 Hampstead High Street, London NW3 1QQ;
4-12 Tattersalls Lane, Melbourne, Victoria 3000,
Australia; Cameron and Kelker Streets, PO Box
1831, Harrisburg, Pennsylvania 17105, USA.

British Library Cataloguing in Publication Data:
Stern, Robert C.
America's fighters of the 1980s: the F-16 and F-18.
–(Warbirds; 17)
1. F-16 (Fighter Planes)
2. Hornet (Jet fighter plane)
I. Title   II. Series
623.74′ 64   UG1242.F5
ISBN 0-85368-578-9

Layout by Anthony A. Evans.
Printed in Great Britain by William Clowes (Beccles)
Limited.

It is proper that the F-16 Fighting Falcon and F-18 Hornet should appear together as the representatives of the latest generation of fighters for the US Air Force and Navy, because their history has been intimately entwined from conception. The ADF programme that gave birth to the F-16 was originally intended to provide a new fighter (essentially an F-4 replacement) for both services. The Navy pulled out of the programme, as it did with the F-111, claiming that its requirements were too different from the USAF's for the needs of both forces to be met by one aircraft. Indeed, the Navy's withdrawal from the programme helped to make it impossible for General Dynamics to meet its cost ceilings with the F-16, leaving it open to much Congressional criticism.

This early Department of Defense intention that the USAF and the Navy should fly the same new fighter was only the first of the connections between the two aircraft featured in this book. A decade after withdrawing from the ADF programme, the Navy decided that a derivative of the loser of the Air Force's new fighter competition would be its choice of fighter for a new decade. The two fighters now find themselves frequently competing against each other, as well as the best new fighters of the rest of the world, for foreign sales contracts. Perhaps the ultimate connection would result if the US Navy chose a modified F-16 to be its new 'Aggressor' aircraft, a very real possibility. Then F-16s would clash with F-18s in simulated combat as well as on paper.

By the end of the decade, these two aircraft combined will easily be the most numerous free-world combat aircraft, equipping at least fifteen air forces. As such, they will be the first line of defence for NATO and its allies against the Soviets. Much, therefore, depends on the quality of the Hornet and Fighting Falcon. It is this author's hope that this book will show that quality to be very high indeed.

A large number of people and organizations have assisted with photographs and information. In particular, I would like to thank Rob Mack and Z. Joe Thornton of General Dynamics and Craig Smith of McDonnell Aircraft for their considerable help; the Public Affairs offices of the 8th TFW, 50th TFW and of the Tactical Fighter Weapons Center, Nellis AFB; and the defence attachés of the embassies of Belgium, the Netherlands and Denmark, who have also supplied photographs.

Robert C. Stern, 1982.

2. The third FSD Hornet passes over USS *America* (CV 66), having completed the Hornet's first series of sea trials on 30 October 1979. The Navy made identification easy by conspicuously numbering the A/F-18 prototypes. (McD-D by Pat McManus)

▲3

▲4　▼5

3-5. In 1965, the USAF requested formal proposals from a number of US aerospace companies for an Advanced Day Fighter (ADF), intended as a counter to the MiG 21s then being met over Vietnam. (No USAF fighter since the F-86 had been intended as an air superiority dog-fighter and the then current-generation F-4s and F-105s found themselves at a disadvantage in low-speed engagements with the more agile MiG.) The new fighter was to be in the 25,000lb weight class and possess low wing loading and a high thrust-to-weight ratio sufficient to offer a 25 per cent margin of superiority over the MiG 21. General Dynamics responded with their Project 401, which set out to find the optimum combination of 78 significant variables, including conventional or blended wing-body shaping, various leading-edge sweep angles and wing shapes, fixed or variable wing camber, side or bottom outlets and single or double tails. Three of the more than 20 basic design 'families' that were considered before the programme was terminated in favour of the Low Cost Fighter (LCF) are seen here in model form. They are the single-tailed, bottom-inlet 401F, the twin-tailed, bottom-inlet 401F-4 and the side-inlet 401FS-1. (GD)

6, 7. The next year (1966), word first arrived of the MiG 25 Foxbat, leading to the realization that no single airframe could be optimized to counter both the MiG 21 and 25. The USAF now needed two fighters: one capable of sustained high-altitude, long-range missile combat with Foxbats, and another optimized for lower, slower and shorter-range combat with MiG 21s. This led to the cancellation of the ADF programme and its replacement by the LCF. The Air Force correctly surmised that Congress would baulk at funding two major fighter development programmes simultaneously and thus emphasized the low cost of the 'low-end' fighter of the 'high-low mix' during its early bouts with legislators. Indeed, the instructions that went out to General Dynamics and others in 1966 was to pare down their ADF designs to fit within a $3 million per copy flyaway cost. Of necessity, this meant a smaller aircraft of lighter weight (about 18,000lb), shorter range and with much reduced avionics. Counterbalancing these reductions would be gains in thrust-to-weight ratio and reduced wing loading, meaning improved manoeuvrability. At Fort Worth this meant a new series of models based on the ADF series, the choice eventually coming down to one between the twin-tailed, conventional-bodied, oval-inlet 404 and the blended-body, conformal-inlet 205C, with the latter obviously getting the final nod. The Air Force gave first priority to the 'high-end' fighter, leading to the F-15 Eagle which flew in 1971. Only then were they ready to decide on an LCF. (GD)

8. A formal RFP (Request for Proposals) for the LCF went out on 6 January 1972. Five companies responded, General Dynamics and Northrop being each awarded contracts for a pair of prototypes. Construction began immediately at Fort Worth on the two YF-16s; the first is seen here as it neared completion on 18 September 1973. (GD)

6▲

7▲ 8▼

▲9 ▼10

9. The second YF-16 (s/n 70-1568) flies formation with a pair of 84th FIS F-106s over Edwards AFB, California in 1974, as the new fighters were 'flown off' against all comers. (The last two digits of the funding year rather than the year of actual completion make up the first two digits of a USAF serial number. To complete the confusion, the first of those digits was generally not shown until the late 1970s.) By the time actual prototypes had been built, it had become obvious that the $3 million cost ceiling could never be maintained and the name of the programme was subtly shifted from LCF to LWF (Light-Weight Fighter). (GD)

10. In January 1975, the USAF decided in favour of the YF-16 (and against the Northrop YF-17), authorizing General Dynamics to build fifteen FSD (Full Scale Development) airframes. The Pratt & Whitney F100 engine was installed in the first FSD airframe in September 1976. The F100 was criticized for being overly complex and too prone to flame-out, but experience has shown it to be reliable and the commonality of power plants with the F-15 has reduced spare part inventories. (GD)

11. Ready except for paint, the first FSD F-16 stands on the work floor at General Dynamics' Fort Worth facility. The dark colour of the vertical and horizontal tail surfaces indicate the extensive use of composite skins, which simultaneously increase strength and reduce weight, October 1976. (GD)

12. When the first FSD airframe (s/n 75-0745) was rolled out on 20 October 1976, it posed for a family portrait with the second YF-16. The similarity of paint scheme belies the fact that these are totally different airframes, the FSD aircraft being marginally larger than the prototypes in all dimensions. The difference is most noticeable in the nose area, which has been bulged to increase internal volume. (GD)

▲13

▲14 ▼15

13. Even after the FSD F-16s began to enter the test programme, the second prototype retained its Bicentennial colour scheme (without the 'Y' on its tail) and continued its role in the test programme. The first prototype meanwhile had been diverted to another duty. This photograph dates from December 1978 during the multinational test phase of F-16 development. (GD)

14. The seventh FSD aircraft and first two-seat F-16B was s/n 75-0751. The 'B' is a fully capable combat aircraft as well as a trainer. Camouflage experiments continued all through 1976. This aircraft wears the three shades of grey eventually adopted, but in a pattern more closely resembling that used on F-15s. (GD)

15. The sixth FSD airframe (s/n 75-0750) shows the camouflage scheme eventually adopted as standard for all USAF F-16s. The forward fuselage is light grey blending into dark grey with a slightly lighter third shade of grey on the undersurfaces. Information markings are black and white; warning markings are salmon pink. The radome here has been painted grey because early production F-16s had black radomes. Later aircraft were completed with grey composite radomes. This airframe would later reappear as the AFTI F-16. (GD)

16. Production at Fort Worth has been uneventful, which is good news for the USAF. Here, the 300th F-16 built by General Dynamics prepares for its delivery flight to MacDill AFB, Florida, 19 December 1980. This was one of the last pre-MSIP Fighting Falcons, the first of those modifications being introduced on the assembly line in 1981, beginning with the 330th example. (GD)

17. The advantage of the blended-wing concept is graphically demonstrated in this view of an early production F-16 at high alpha (angle of attack). Condensation spirals trailing back from the forebody strake show the strong, controlled vortex flow, which both reduces tail drag and improves directional stability by delaying vortex breakdown until well aft of the tail surface. (GD)

16▲ 17▼

18. Testing of the F-16 has continued unabated. Here, an early production model (note the black radome) is removed from a 30ft-high wooden platform at Kirtland AFB, New Mexico, where it had been undergoing nuclear hardness testing, May 1980. (GD)

19-21. 'Iron bombs' can be carried on one or a pair of pylons under each wing. Each pylon can carry a single Mk. 84 2,000lb bomb or three (outboard) or six (inboard) Mk. 82 500lb bombs. The F-16's accuracy with unguided bombs is nearly four times greater than the F-4's and considerably better than the A-7's and F-111's. Again it is the Israelis who have put this to the test, demonstrating the Fighting Falcon's incredible accuracy with 'slicks' in the June 1981 raid on the Osirak reactor near Baghdad. (GD)

▲18 ▼19

22. The F-16's standard weapons are the GE M61A-1 20mm cannon in the forward fuselage and a pair of AIM-9 Sidewinder heat-seeking missiles mounted on wing tip rails. The AIM-9L, the latest version of the venerable Sidewinder, has proved itself still extremely potent as recently as the Lebanese War of July–August 1982. (GD)

20▲

21▲   22▼

▲23

▲24 ▼25

26▲   27▲

23–27. A variety of laser-guided weapons can be delivered by currently configured F-16s with the use of add-on laser tracking pods. In testing at Edwards AFB, California, the second prototype was fitted with an ATLIS (Automatic Tracking Laser Illumination System – incorporating a helmet mounted sight – guidance pod and became the first single-seat aircraft to designate targets successfully and guide such weapons to a target. The weapons included KMU-guided standard Mk. 83 1,000lb bombs and the more advanced TI-built GBU-16/B with extended rear fins, modified from the same basic bomb. In each case the aircraft made a 4g turn after bomb release, January 1979. MSIP II F-16s are intended to be equipped with LANTIRN (Low-Altitude navigation – Targetting IR for Night) pods faired into the intake, one of which will house a laser designator similar to that of the ATLIS system. (GD)

▲28

▲29　▼30

28. The GEPOD-30 has been successfully ground tested at Fort Worth suspended from this nearly completed airframe, early 1982. The heavy-handed retouching of the upper surfaces of the aircraft in this photograph occurred because an Israeli F-16 airframe was used for these tests, a fact the USAF did not wish to publicize at the time. The cannon in the GEPOD-30 is GE's 30mm four-barrel GPU-5/A. (GD)

29, 30. The Hughes AMRAAM (Advanced Medium-Range Air-to-Air Missile), chosen as the intended successor to the AIM-7 Sparrow, was successfully test-fired against a QF-102 drone on 26 August 1981. The test aircraft is from the 3246th Test Wing based at Eglin AFB, Florida. (GD)

31. The 1st FSD (Full Scale Development) F-16 (s/n 75-0745) as it appeared in 1976. It being the Bicentennial year, the paint scheme was unabashedly 'red, white and blue'. The flags of the US, the four European Consortium nations and Iran (these were the days of the Shah, when Iran was probably the largest foreign purchaser of US arms) are proudly displayed. (GD)

32. The first MSIP I (Multi-national Staged Improvement Program, Phase I) F-16s differed visually from earlier models solely in the larger tailplane, which was introduced to offset the heavier avionics that will be part of MSIP II and to help give the aircraft a nose-up attitude in case of computer failure. (GD)

16

▲33 ▼34

33. The first prototype of the A/F-18 stands on the apron at St. Louis on a wet dawn in April 1979. Only the first Hornet carried this three-colour scheme with both its name and symbol emblazoned on its fuselage. (McD-D)

34. The ten remaining FSD (Full Scale Development) Hornets sported a more sedate blue and white scheme. The A/F-18 has had a particularly troublesome development history with cost over-runs and failure to meet a number of performance parameters early in the programme, leading to even more Congressional criticism than usual for a new weapons system. Tremendous effort on the part of McDonnell Douglas and the Navy has solved most of the outstanding problems, with the notable exception of high cost, making the Hornet's future more secure. (McD-D)

35-38. A sequence of photographs showing the destruction of the QF-102 drone by the first guided launch of the Hughes AMRAAM by a 3246th Test Wing F-16 on 26 August 1981. The Hughes missile has since won the AMRAAM competition and has entered production. (Hughes)

39. A TV-guided AGM-65 Maverick was successfully test-fired in August 1979 from the first FSD F-16B at China Lake, California. Nevertheless, F-16s will probably never carry Mavericks in combat because the target acquisition process for the Maverick is better suited to a slower aircraft, such as the A-10. (GD)

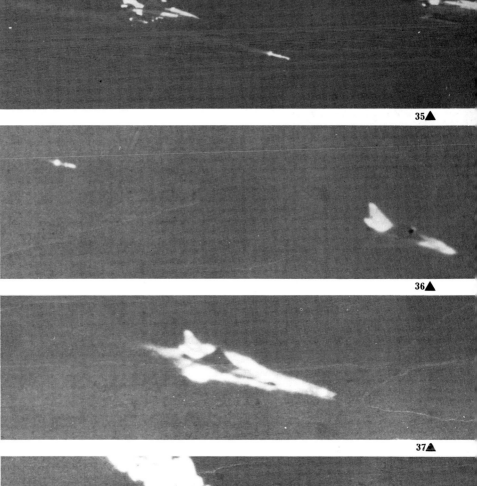

35▲

36▲

37▲

38▲ 39▼

▲40

▲41 ▼42

F-16A COCKPIT ARRANGEMENT
BLOCK 24 JUNE 1979

40. The F-16A's cockpit has been described as the best fighter cockpit ever designed, with its 30° angled seat, side-stick controller (right side), well-placed instrumentation and exceptional visibility. The 'standard' F-16 is equipped with a 9 × 13° Head-Up Display, the largest HUD achievable at the time of the F-16's design. (GD)

41. The layout of the F-16A's cockpit is straightforward. At the top is the HUD and immediately below that the HUD controls. Normal flight instrumentation (altimeter, engine gauges, etc.) are clustered below and to the right. To the left is the Stores Control Panel and above that the threat warning azimuth indicator. At the bottom, between the pilot's legs is the REO (Radar/Electro-Optical) display. The left corner panel contains landing gear and flap controls, the right has the fuel tank select switches, back-up compass and system warning lights. The left side panel is mainly given over to radar controls and the FCNP (Fire Control/Navigation Panel), the right side panel to radio and cockpit environment controls. On the far left is the throttle, while the side-stick controller is on the right. The throttle handle and stick include controls for most basic radar and weapons delivery functions, meaning most flight situations can be handled without the pilot having to remove his hands from those two controls. (GD)

42. The Westinghouse AN/APG-66 has been the centre of most of the criticism of the F-16, mainly because of its limited (approximately 30nm) range. This goes back to the original LCF specification and its 'downgraded' avionics and represents no failure on the part of the radar to meet all requirements. Nevertheless, improving the APG-66 is central to MSIP (Multinational Staged Improvement Program). MSIP I aircraft, which are currently coming off the production line, have an enlarged tailplane and cooling for the avionics bay. (Pre-MSIP F-16s have no avionics bay refrigeration, which limits power usage and, consequently, radar range.) The pilot MSIP II aircraft is to leave the Fort Worth assembly line in July 1984. MSIP II will include improved, longer-range radar, LANTIRN and an enlarged Marconi HUD. (GD)

43. Models showing the
smaller, original tailplane
(left) and the enlarged unit.
Due to advances in composite
technology, the new unit is
lighter and less expensive to
build than the smaller
tailplane. The rear corners are
clipped to aid ground
clearance on take-off. (GD)
44. An artist's conception of
the front cockpit of an MSIP
II F-16. The 30 × 18° HUD
being developed by Marconi
stretches the limits of HUD
technology by a considerable
margin, allowing 'life-sized'
image projection. The pilot
will see FLIR imagery
generated by LANTIRN
identical in size to what he
would normally see in clear
weather. The new instru-
mentation will feature two
radar CRTs for the projection
of searching and targeting
information simultaneously.
(GD)

43▲   44▼

▲45 ▼46

47▲

45. An MSIP I F-16 is caught in flight, showing the enlarged tailplane, the only external distinguishing mark. (GD)

46, 47. The first prototype (s/n 70-1567) was modified very early in the test programme into the CCV (Controlled Configured Vehicle) test bed. The first flight (seen here) was made on 16 March 1976. A pair of large canards are canted at 30° from the intake. These could rotate through 25°, allowing level turning without side slip, raising/lowering of the nose without changing the flight path and lateral or vertical translation (changing the flight path without altering the aircraft's attitude). These new capabilities simplified target tracking immeasurably, seemingly pointing the way to the next generation of fighter aircraft. The success of the CCV, which was otherwise unmodified for its new role, led to the desire for fuller testing with the more extensively altered AFTI F-16. (GD)

▲48 ▼49

48. The AFTI (Advanced Fighter Technology Integration) F-16 flew for the first time on 10 July 1982. Developed from the sixth FSD airframe, the AFTI airframe integrates the angled canards of the CCV with advanced avionics including limited voice-actuation of controls, the extra electronics being housed in the dorsal spine. The camouflage is a wavy pattern of standard USAF light and dark greys. (GD)

49. The eighth FSD airframe (s/n 75-0752), the second F-16B, has been modified to accept an alternative power plant, the J79-GE-119. The normally powered F-16 is either unattractive or 'off limits' to many potential customers for a number of reasons, including the desire of the US government to limit Third World (and Soviet) access to the high-technology F100 engine, and sheer engine cost. The J79 is a logical alternative engine, being well known and widely used around the world (being the standard engine of the F-104 and F-4). The January 1980 decision of the State Department to offer an FX (low-cost export fighter – an F-5E replacement) to Third World nations led to a production go-ahead at Fort Worth. (GD)

50. The rear sections of the F-16/79 and a standard F100-powered F-16 are contrasted here. The actual conversion to the J79 was eased considerably by the nearly identical diameter of the two engines. Only the increased length of the J79 had to be accommodated, hence the extended tail fairing. The lesser air requirements of the J79 were accounted for by a minor reshaping and reduction in the area of the intake. (GD)

51. The F-16/79 flew for the first time on 29 October 1980 and completed its flight testing in January 1981. The lower power output of the J79 compared to that of the F100 (18,000lb st vs. 25,000lb st) has surprisingly little effect on the aircraft's basic performance. The F-16/79 still has a top speed of Mach 2, though the acceleration and manoeuvrability are, understandably, less than that of the standard F-16. Most importantly, the price tag is about $1 million less than that of a standard model. (GD)

50▲ 51▼

▼52 ▲53

52. Considering the history of the LCF/LWF programme, and the effect of the Navy's withdrawal from it, there could hardly be more irony in the Navy's recent interest in buying F-16/79s to replace its F-5E/F Aggressor aircraft. The F-16/79 demonstrator was tested during early 1982 by VX-4 at MCAS Yuma and by VF-43 at NAS Oceana. For the Yuma tests, the F-16/79 was given VX-4's XF tail code and a Top Gun badge. The Navy plans to make a decision on a new Aggressor aircraft in time for inclusion in the 1984 budget. (GD)

53. The first FSD airframe (s/n 75-0745) also received an alternative engine, the F101DFE (Derivative Fighter Engine).

The F101 was the engine developed to power the 'on-again-off-again' B-1 bomber. When that programme was cancelled by President Carter, the Department of Defense decided to try to get some use out of the engine by developing its core section into a fighter power plant. (GD)

54. The future of the F-16/101 is probably dependent on the results of testing the DFE in the F-14. The problems with the Tomcat's TF30 engines have far outweighed those of the F100, and any production decision on the DFE for F-16s will probably depend on whether or not the Navy chooses to re-engine its Tomcats. (GD)

▲55

▲56 ▼57

55. The F101DFE also proved easy to fit into the F-16, being only slightly larger than the F100. During testing, which was conducted between December 1980 and July 1981, the only problem encountered was a high-frequency vibration in the inlet at low power, which was solved by increasing the throttle idle settings. The higher power of the DFE (28,000lb st) was entirely beneficial, improving the F-16's thrust-to-weight ratio even further. (GD)

56. Early in the development of the F-16, the notion of a supersonic cruise version was mooted. This early model shows that the idea of a 'cranked arrow' wing was basic to the concept.

57-58. The fifth FSD airframe (s/n 75-0749) was taken in hand for modification to supersonic cruise configuration, the conversion being completed in time for roll-out on 2 July 1982. To demonstrate the tremendous load-carrying capabilities of the F-16XL, the prototype carried sixteen Mk. 82s, four AMRAAMs and a pair of Sidewinders. The 'XL' is the first USAF F-16 to be fitted with the extended tail fairing/drag chute housing introduced by the Norwegians. This will become standard on future Fort Worth-built F-16s. (GD)

59. The first flight of the 'XL' came on 6 July 1982. A 'fly-off' against the F-15 Strike Eagle began in the autumn with the winner expected to receive a major contract in 1984. The F-16XL fuselage is stretched 56in, increasing fuel capacity by 82 per cent and giving an additional 40 cubic feet for avionics. The additional lift generated by the new wing will shorten take-off runs by a third, increase combat radius by 45 per cent and double the effective weapons load. (GD)

60. The first unit to equip with the Fighting Falcon was the 388th TFW based at Hill AFB, Utah. The transition from F-4 Phantom to F-16 went smoothly, despite the tremendous differences in the two aircraft. As is typical, this first unit assumed the responsibility of working up the new fighter and then training all successive units to form on the new aircraft. From the time of the delivery of the first F-16 to Hill AFB in January 1979 to the present, the 388th's four component squadrons have been testing the Falcon's capabilities, particularly in the ground attack role. Four 2,000lb Mk. 84 'slicks' drop from this 421st TFS F-16A, which also carries the rarely seen centreline fuel tank. (GD)

61. F-16s from the 34th TFS line up on the apron at Hill AFB. As the F-16 has developed, the number of additions, particularly on the tail, has increased. Threat warning antennae are now located above and below the rudder. Formation and anti-collision lights are located on the rudder actuator housing and on top of the tail. (USAF)

62. At the beginning of a busy day at Hill, armourers bring pallets of Mk. 82 500lb bombs out to the flight-line. The yellow band around the nose section of these 'slicks' indicates that they are live munitions rather than the more common, blue-painted, inert bombs. The tail bands on these F16s of the 4th TFS are yellow with a black thunderbolt. (GD)

63. The second operational unit to receive F-16s was the 56th TFW at MacDill AFB, Florida. Two of their aircraft are seen here cruising over the Gulf of Mexico. The CO's mount has a four-coloured band and is accompanied by a red-banded F-16A. The 56th naturally became responsible for F-16 advanced training, because of MacDill's relative proximity to the USAF's weapons test unit at Eglin AFB. (GD)

▲60   ▼61

62▲   63▼

▲64

64. The 474th TFW at Nellis AFB, Nevada, was the third operational F-16 unit and the first without training or testing responsibilities. (USAF)

65. The 428th TFS (blue tail band with white skull-and-crossbones), the first squadron of the 474th to convert to F-16s, transitioned from F-4s in November 1980. (GD)

66. The other unit at Nellis to receive F-16s was the 57th Fighter Weapons Wing/Detachment 16. The tail band is yellow and black chequer-board. Originally formed as the MOT&E (Multinational

Operational Test & Evaluation) unit at Hill AFB, the detachment is now part of the 57th at Nellis, which operates other aircraft types besides the F-16. (GD)

67. At high alpha and low altitude on a humid day, this 57th TWW F-16 trails magnificent spiral contrails from the forward strakes. The absence of wing tip contrails indicates how successful the F-16's designers have been in reducing drag-producing wing tip vortices. (GD)

▼65

66▲ 67▼

68. The 363rd TFW at Shaw AFB, South Carolina is the latest CONUS unit to begin re-equipping with F-16s, which are to replace the unit's Phantoms. Here, the old and new COs' aircraft fly formation, 1982. In keeping with the new DoD policy of equipping Guard and Reserve units with first-line equipment rather than obsolescent 'hand-me-downs', the next CONUS units to receive F-16s will be the 169th TFG of the South Carolina ANG at McEntire ANG Base (replacing A-7s) and the 466th TFS of the AFRES at Hill AFB (replacing F-105s). Both units will convert to the new aircraft in 1983. (GD)

69. The first overseas deployment of F-16s was to the 8th TFW 'Wolfpack' at Kunsan AB, Republic of Korea. Transition from F-4s began there in June 1981. The 8th is one of the oldest and

most illustrious units in the USAF and, as such, is rare in rating a tail code unrelated to the name of its base. Also unusual is the wolf's head insignia carried by all 8th TFW aircraft. The PACAF badge is carried on the tail. (USAF)

70. A two-seat F-16B (J-259) of the Royal Netherlands Air Force cruises over the Dutch coastline, May 1979. By the end of March 1982 the Luchtmacht was operating 57 of its planned purchase of 213 F-16s. (KLL)

71. FA-14 of 349 Sqn., 1 Wing, Belgian Air Force, is based at Beauvechain. (The serial indicates that this is the fourteenth F-16A in the Belgian inventory.) The Belgians have 116 F-16s in stock or on order and are considering the purchase of an additional 44 to replace their ageing Mirage 5s. (FAB)

▲72 ▼73

74▲

72. The 388th TFW, given the task of proving the Fighting Falcon's worth as a ground attacker, experimentally repainted a pair of 34th TFS aircraft in A-10-style 'charcoal lizard' (officially known as the European I scheme) camouflage during 1980. The change was very unpopular with pilots at Hill AFB, who are fiercely proud of their fighters' ACM capabilities and did not want to become typecast as 'mud beaters'. The experiment was never repeated. (GD)

73. In recent years, the US Navy has moved away from its traditionally colourful markings schemes, adopting a two-tone light grey camouflage and restricting all other insignia, including the national insignia and emergency markings, to a darker shade of grey. Here, the CO's aircraft of VFA-125, the first operational unit to receive Hornets, is seen over Southern California, June 1981. (McD-D)

74. Unit pride runs strong with the 8th. The outboard cargo pod is emblazoned with unit and PACAF badges and the name 'Wolfpack'. The tail band is blue, indicating the 80th TFS. (GD)

75. A pair of Wolfpack Fighting Falcons formate over the Pacific. PACAF is enthusiastic about the F-16 and will be converting a second squadron, the 51st TFW at Osan AB, starting in 1983. (GD)

75▼

▲76

▲77 ▼78

76. The first USAFE unit to convert to F-16s was the 313th TFS of the 50th TFW, Hahn AB, West Germany; conversion began in late 1981. The hard shelter is a feature of all USAF bases in Europe. (USAF)

77. USAFE expressed considerable concern about the short range of the F-16's radar and, therefore, its suitability to the European environment. The promised improvements of MSIP, the proven ability to fire the new AMRAAM and the success of the Israelis with their F-16s have all helped to wear down USAFE's resistance. (USAF)

78. A foggy dawn at Hahn. While still too early for a final verdict, the experience of the 50th to date has shown the F-16 fully capable of handling the often poor weather in Europe. Current plans call for the 86th TFW at Ramstein AB, West Germany, to be the next USAFE unit to convert to F-16s. (USAF)

79. Clothed in ABC gear, two groundcrewmen reload the 20mm cannon with a 'Dragon' automatic loader, just outside a hard shelter at Hahn. More than in any other theatre, USAFE must prepare constantly to operate in the most adverse of environments, man-made as well as natural. (GD)

80, 81. Far from the heat of the Utah desert, twelve F-16s of the 4th TFS, 388th TFW, participate in Exercise 'Coronet Wrangler', March 1981. For a full month, the dozen USAF Falcons were based at Flesland Air Station near Bergen, Norway. There they co-operated with Norwegian F-16s and F-5s in a variety of missions, with detached operations from Bodo and Andoya, north of the Arctic Circle, completing over 300 sorties in total. The deployment and return flights, over ten hours in length, were accomplished non-stop with three refuellings each way. (A similar sortie in F-4s would have used five times the fuel.) (GD)

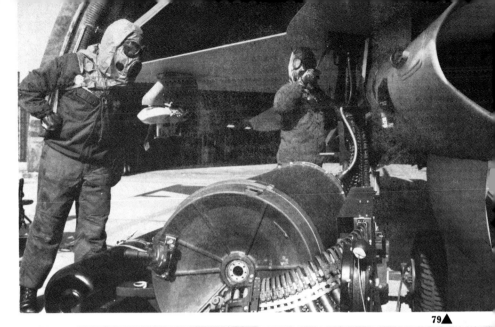

79▲

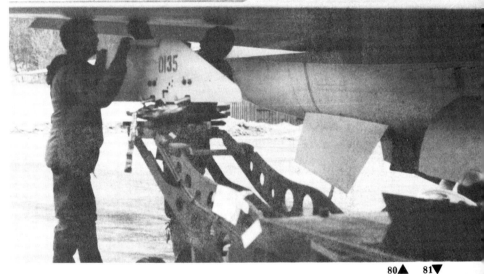

80▲ 81▼

▲82 ▼83

82, 83. Part of the job of convincing USAFE to accept F-16s was done by a team of seven 388th TFW Falcons from Hill AFB during the annual RAF bombing competition held at RAF Lossiemouth during June 1981. Besides the F-16s, USAF F-111s, two teams of RAF Jaguars and one of RN Buccaneers participated in the meet. The F-16s scored 7,831 out of a possible 8,000 points, outscoring the second-place Jaguar team by 1,074 points. Against simulated air-to-air threats, F-16s scored 88 'kills' while suffering no 'losses'. The other teams cumulatively had 42 'losses' and one 'kill'. 388th groundcrews averaged 10.5 minutes turn-around time to load six Mk. 82 bombs and 515 rounds of 20mm ammunition. (GD)

84, 85. The first F-16s delivered to each of the four European Consortium air forces pose for the cameras, January 1980. The decision by Belgium, the Netherlands, Denmark and Norway to co-ordinate their fighter procurement led to one of the most important fighter competitions in history, between the SAAB Viggen, Dassault Mirage F.1, Northrop YF-17 and the YF-16. The decision in May 1977 in favour of the F-16 has led to the first truly multinational aircraft programme, with assembly taking place in three countries and component manufacture in five. Since the original decision to procure 348 aircraft, two of the Consortium members have increased their orders which, along with a share of the orders received from the five other nations who have ordered standard F-16s, will keep the European assembly lines open for years to come. This is not to say that this unique co-production arrangement has always worked flawlessly. There have been complaints from some Consortium members, particularly Denmark, of uneven work distribution. Still, the overwhelming good sense of five NATO member nations flying the same aircraft and the basic qualities of the F-16 itself have kept such problems to a minimum. (GD)

▲86 ▼87

88▲

89▲ 90▼

86. The Royal Netherlands Air Force (KLL – Koninklijke Nederlandse Luchtmacht) will eventually be the largest European operator of F-16s, with current planning calling for five squadrons of Fighting Falcons. J-212 is part of the first Dutch squadron, 322 Sqn. based at Leeuwarden AB. The next squadron to form on the F-16 will be 323 Sqn. (also at Leeuwarden), to be followed by 306, 311 and 312 Sqns. at Volkel. (KLL)

87. Dutch F-16s look identical to their USAF counterparts except for the national insignia and tail codes. This 322 Sqn. Falcon is wearing the same three shades of grey as US aircraft. The four-colour roundel is in four positions, once on each side of the fuselage and on the port upper and starboard lower wing surfaces. (KLL)

88, 89. Both sides of J-218. European production F-16s retained the black radome longer than did US production models, only switching over to the grey radome late in 1980. (KLL)

90. As 322 Sqn. worked up at Leeuwarden, new aircraft with grey radomes began to fill out the squadron. Note also the reduced size of the fuselage roundel. Since the unit was declared operational in mid-1981, a few of its F-16s have been seen sporting the squadron's Grey Parrot patch on the tail. (J. E. Jose)

▲91 ▼92

93▲

91. The Belgian Air Force (FAB – Force Aérienne Belge) will eventually fly two wings of F-16s. Like the Dutch, they have increased their original order, now planning on a buy of 160. Here, a pair of Belgian Falcons patrol the North Sea, including a recent production model (note the grey radome). When all new F-16s have the extended tail fairing introduced by the Norwegians, the FAB will house a Loral Rapport III ECM system there in place of a drag chute, replacing the external ECM pods carried by USAF F-16s. (FAB)

92. The Belgians had originally inteded to paint their F-16s like their F-104s, in a brown, green and grey camouflage scheme, but they too have chosen to follow USAF practice. Here, four 349 Sqn. Fighting Falcons formate over low clouds. The lead aircraft is a newer model with a grey radome. (FAB)

93. Over the rugged Ardennes, FA-14 banks away from the camera, showing a standard load of four AIM-9Ls. This aircraft is part of 349 Sqn., 1 Wing, the first F-16 squadron to qualify for NATO service in January 1981. A second wing, 10 Wing at Kleine Brogel, will be re-equipped with F-16s after all units of 1 Wing have converted. (FAB)

▲94

▲95 ▼96

94. A pair of FAB F-16s scramble from Beauvechain during 349 Sqn.'s qualification testing, 1981. Landing gear retraction must commence immediately after rotation or the maximum permissible retraction airspeed will be exceeded, so fast is the acceleration of an F-16 at take-off power. (FAB)

95. The Royal Norwegian Air Force (KNL – Kongelige Norske Flyvapen) has ordered 72 F-16s and had received 35 as of the end of March 1982. All are characterized by the extended tail fairing used to house a drag chute, introduced to help shorten landing roll-out on Norway's short and often icy runways. This feature was incorporated on all three assembly lines during 1982-83. Eventually, three squadrons of the KNL will fly F-16s, 331 and 334 Sqns. at Bodo and 332 Sqn. at Rygge. Alone among the Consortium nations, Norway's F-16s carry a different camouflage, an overall light grey. (GD)

96. A Royal Danish Air Force (KDF – Kongelige Danske Flyvevaben) F-16B caught just as the gear doors are closing. The camouflage is USAF-style with six-position red-and-white roundels and the Danish flag on the tail. (GD)

97. The first KDF unit to complete formation is 727 Sqn. based at Skydstrup. Note the squadron badge just behind the radome. By the end of March 1982, the KDF had received 36 of its 58 F-16s. (KDF)

98, 99. This F-16B was the first for the Israeli Air Force (IAF – Heyl Ha'Avir) and was delivered in January 1980. While other air forces have at times been equivocal in their response to the F-16, the IAF has been enthusiastic from the beginning. Having received all 75 of their original order, the Israelis have now requested the same number again. The camouflage is standard IAF: brown, sand and light green upper surfaces with light blue-grey undersides. (GD)

97▲

98▲ 99▼

47

100. The first 'formal' delivery did not take place until the third Israeli airframe was handed over on 31 January 1980. While the Carter and Reagan Administrations have been frustrated by what is seen as the unpredictability of Israeli military actions, at times holding up the delivery of F-16s (and now delaying approval of the second half of Israel's order), the USAF has benefitted greatly from IAF experience with the Fighting Falcon in the Osirak Raid and in the war over Lebanon. Being the only nation to have used F-16s (or F-15s for that matter) in actual combat, the IAF has much knowledge to share. Their unabated enthusiasm for the F-16 speaks volumes. (GD)

101, 102. The latest nation to receive the Fighting Falcon is Egypt, which has ordered 40 and had received eight as of 31 March 1982. The second aircraft, seen here, was delivered in January 1982. This is an MSIP I airframe; note the enlarged tailplane. The red numerals on the intake are a factory number that was removed before actual delivery. The first EAF F-16 squadron was activated at An Shas AB, Egypt, in March 1982. (GD)

▼100

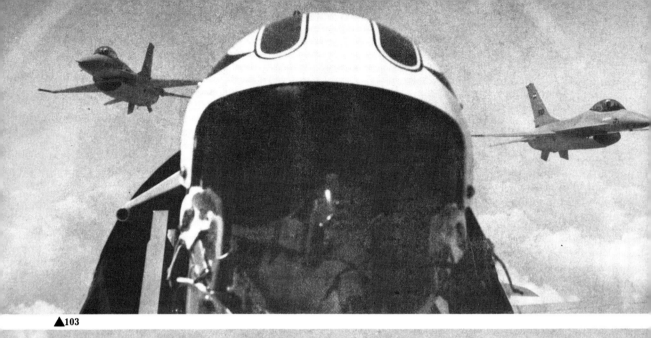

▲103

104▲ 105▼

103. The first three Egyptian F-16s were ferried across the Atlantic in March 1982 en route to their permanent base at An Shas. Note the serial repeated in 'Arabic' numerals on the nose. A further three countries (South Korea, Venezuela and Pakistan) have been approved to receive the standard Fighting Falcon. Greece and Turkey are considering the F-16 as their next fighter. (GD)

104. As part of the joint Egyptian–US exercise, 'Bright Star', three Egyptian F-16s and three USAF F-15s were ferried across the Atlantic. Here, the flight poses with a KC-135 tanker prior to refuelling. The trio of Fighting Falcons carry 'strip-off' USAF markings on their wings, required for the international flight. (GD)

105. One that got away from General Dynamics but, as has happened in two other cases, GD's loss was McDonnell Douglas's gain. The three head-to-head competitions between the F-16 and F-18 for fighter contracts (Canada, Australia and Spain) have all been won by the Hornet. The reasons given in each case have been based on the F-18's two engines and longer range radar. (GD)

▲106 ▼107

106. The loser of the LWF competition was the Northrop YF-17 Cobra. To a much larger extent, the real loser has been the Northrop Corporation, which is getting only limited benefit from the subsequent success of the derivative F-18. After the Navy's decision to pull out of the LWF programme, Northrop agreed with McDonnell Douglas that the latter would develop a naval version of the F-17 (the F-18 Hornet), while Northrop would continue to market the Cobra (as the F-18L). To Northrop's chagrin, the F-18L finds itself in competition not only with the F-16 but also with the Hornet, a more capable if more expensive aircraft. Not surprisingly, the Cobra has yet to win a contract. One of the YF-17 prototypes has been retained by Northrop; here it is painted in Spanish colours before that

nation's fighter competition was narrowed to the F-16 and F-18 and finally to the Hornet alone. (Northrop)

107. After McDonnell Douglas won the Navy's contract to develop a navalized YF-17, the Northrop prototype flew briefly in these colours, two shades of blue and white. Despite being labelled the F-18 prototype, this is an unmodified YF-17. While very similar in external appearance, the actual F-18 is a major redesign of the Cobra. (Northrop)

108. While the first F-18 was still under construction, the Navy began in-flight testing of its Hughes AN/APG-65 radar attached to the nose of a specially modified North American T-39D Sabreliner. This rather unusual expedient allowed the radar to be tested under realistic conditions long before a flying F-18 test bed would be

available. (McD-D) :MOD4.

109. A Marine technician looks on as a Hughes engineer adjusts the connections on an early example of the Hornet's APG-65 radar. Not constrained by either the cost or weight limitations placed on the original APG-66 for the F-16, the Hornet's radar is superior in most performance aspects. In particular, it has BVR (Beyond Visual Range) target acquisition capabilities and the search-while-track mode needed to properly guide Sparrows and AMRAAMs. The Improved APG-66 that will be installed in MSIP II F-16s will be the APG-65's equal in these respects, but the superiority of the 'off-the-shelf' F-18's radar has been an important factor in its recent competition victories. (Hughes)

▲110 ▼111

110. The first true F-18 (BuNo 160775) was rolled out in September 1978. Its basic similarity to the YF-17 is immediately obvious. The most noticeable differences are the squared off fin tips and reshaped LEX (Leading Edge Extension). Subtler differences include a larger nose to cover the bigger APG-65 radar and beefed-up landing gear. This first Hornet prototype carried a distinctive colour scheme, overall white with gold and blue stripes on LEX, wings and fins. The name and symbol of the Hornet appear on both sides. (McD-D)

111, 112. The more substantial landing gear of the Hornet, in comparison with that of the YF-17, was required by the stresses of flight deck operations. This, combined with the generally greater airframe strength required for naval operations led to an increase in gross weight to 35,000lb, a jump of more than 10,000lb. While the additional strength and weapons capabilities brought by this extra weight are beneficial, they have not been sufficiently offset by increased engine power. The F-18 is powered by two GE F404s rated at 16,000lb st each, an increase of only about 1,000lb st per engine over the YF-17's two YJ101s (from which the F404 was derived). As a result, the Hornet has been justifiably accused of being under-powered. (McD-D)

113. Only after the second Hornet (BuNo 160776) joined the testing programme did the first prototype acquire a '1' on its fins and nose. Because the F-18 was a derivative programme, the initial airframe was used exclusively for 'proof of type' testing, individual systems testing beginning with the second prototype. The first two F-18s pose together at NATC Patuxent River (more often shortened to Pax River), Maryland, where new and old naval aircraft are tested. (Northrop)

112▲   113▼

▲114 ▼115

127▲   128▼

▲130

129 (previous spread)–**131.** Four production F-18s were delivered to NAS LeMoore, California, in October 1981 to form the nucleus of VFA-125, the initial Hornet training squadron. (It is normal Navy practice to establish a training squadron for a new type on each coast, one to serve the Pacific Fleet and one the Atlantic. Now serving as the training unit for all Hornet IPs (Instructor Pilots), VFA-125 will eventually become one of the two Hornet training squadrons.) Hornets passed their 9,000-hour mark in June 1982. (McD-D)

▼131

132. On its way back from the Paris Air Show of 1981, this Hornet stopped at the Canadian Forces Base at Soellingen, West Germany, giving many CAF pilots a first look at their new mount. The Canadians (and Australians and Spanish) chose the F-18 over the F-16 primarily because of its two engines and its superior radar, and despite its considerably higher cost (approximately double that of an F-16). Whether Greece and Turkey, now facing a similar choice, will make the same decision remains to be seen. MSIP II F-16s, which should be available in 1984, will closely match the F-18 in radar performance, making for an even closer race between the aircraft. Both aircraft are effective multi-mission tactical fighters, with a definite edge in manoeuvrability and power over the F-16 and in survivability over the F-18. These differences reflect a real dissimilarity between the needs of the USAF and the Navy. USAF needed a dogfighter with superlative attack capabilities and has it in the Fighting Falcon. The Navy, with a greater need to ensure the survival of airframe and crew, was willing to sacrifice power and manoeuvrability (and economy). The USAF fights over land, where a pilot can 'punch out' at any time and expect to survive and where the supply of replacement aircraft is limited only by the on-hand reserve of airframes. The Navy fights over water where a pilot's chances of survival after bailing out are always much chancier and where replacement of downed aircraft in battle is impossible. For this reason, the Navy must place more emphasis on getting its damaged aircraft back onboard. (McD-D)

133. The first Canadian F-18 in final assembly at St. Louis, May 1982. The Canadians have elected to have all 138 of their Hornets assembled by McDonnell Douglas rather than setting up their own assembly line, because of the cost savings involved. The fuselage of all Hornets, from the rear of the cockpit back to the tail, is assembled by Northrop as prime subcontractor. The wings, horizontal tail and forward fuselage are added by McDonnell during final assembly. (McD-D)

132▲ 133▼

▲134
134. The first Canadian Hornet, a two-seat F-18B, was rolled out on 28 July 1982. The markings are every bit as subdued as the US Navy's, although the pattern of the greys is different. (McD-D).
135. The first Canadian Hornet flew for the first time the next day, 29 July 1982. Note the false cockpit in black on the

underside of the nose. This idea, reputed to have been the brainchild of aviation artist Keith Ferris, was tried by the US Navy and rejected. Supposedly, the false cockpit can deceive a distant pilot as to which direction the aircraft is facing. (McD-D)

▼135

114, 115. The second airframe was painted in the more sedate (and useful) dark blue and white scheme carried by all other Hornet prototypes. (The sharply contrasting colours bisecting the flying surfaces made it possible to visually track the movement and attitude of the aircraft at long range.) Testing with the second prototype began to reveal some of the problems resulting from the airframe being under-powered. These included reduced combat radius and disappointing acceleration and manoeuvrability. In each of these areas, the early FSD airframes failed to meet the Navy's specifications for its new fighter, putting the Hornet programme under a cloud from which it is now just beginning to emerge. (Northrop & McD-D)

116, 117. The third prototype (BuNo 160777) was selected to conduct the Hornet's first sea trials. These complex series of tests are designed to prove whether an aircraft is suitable for carrier operations. Not only must an aircraft be able to fly on and off the carrier, but it must be compatible with all of a carrier's systems, be capable of easy movement on deck, elevator and hangar and must be easily serviced and armed in a carrier's cramped quarters. The Hornet passed with flying colours these initial tests on USS *America* in October 1979. In fact, one of the F-18's strongest selling points has been the enthusiasm of the fleet for a single, reasonably sized airframe intended to replace both the F-4 Phantom as interdictor and the A-7 Corsair II as a dedicated attacker. (McD-D)

118. As well as conducting the first sea trials, the third prototype was also used for cross-wind landing tests at Edwards AFB during July 1980. Intended from the outset to equip Marine as well as Navy squadrons, the Hornet has had to prove itself in environments as diverse as carrier decks and open desert. (McD-D)

116▲

117▲ 118▼

▲119 ▼120

119. Nine 1,000lb Mk. 83 'slicks' fall from the fourth prototype (BuNo 160778), which began attack systems tests in 1980. The Hornet failed to meet a number of performance specifications early in the test programme, therefore it has undergone considerably greater modification than did the F-16 during its qualification. Most of the changes have been made to the horizontal flying surfaces. The leading edge geometry of the wing and horizontal tail have been altered to improve roll rate (at the cost of slightly increased transonic drag) and the span of the ailerons increased. More noticeable is the disappearance of the leading edge sawtooth on both wing and tail that all the early airframes featured on completion. (This photograph dates from September 1981.) (McD-D)

120. The first two-seater was actually the seventh Hornet (BuNo 160781). The F-18B is fully combat capable, like the F-16, differing from the 'A' only in length. (McD-D)

121, 122. The eighth single-seat Hornet (BuNo 160783) was the first to feature all of the changes in wing and LEX (Leading Edge Extension) that mark full production F-18s. The outer wing panels have been stiffened to increase control stick response and the bleed holes in the LEX plugged to decrease drag. The result of these changes have gone far toward solving the Hornet's performance deficiencies. Its top speed is still lower than wished (Mach 1.8), but acceleration and manoeuvrability are now acceptable and range is up to specifications. (McD-D)

121▲ 122▼

▲123 ▼124

123, 124. To demonstrate the range of the modified Hornet, an early production example (BuNo 161248) flew an unrefuelled mission carrying four 1,000lb Mk. 83 bombs over a radius of 620 miles, October 1981. The aircraft also carried two AIM-9 Sidewinders, three external fuel tanks and a pair of ECM pods, so as to simulate a normal combat load. This aircraft carries the production two-tone grey camouflage (a slightly darker grey is used for the anti-glare panel). The Navy greys are lighter and 'warmer' than the corresponding USAF colours. (McD-D)
125. Included in the continuing testing of the Hornet was this climatic test at the USAF's McKinley Climatic Laboratory, Eglin AFB, Florida, March 1981. This is the thirteenth Hornet, the second full production example (BuNo 161216). At this point in the testing, the Hornet was being deluged by rain at the rate of 20in per hour. The tests also included extremes of heat and cold. (McD-D)

126. To simulate the stresses of carrier landings, an early airframe was reserved for drop testing. The varying strains encountered by an aircraft during an arrested landing on a carrier deck are simulated by altering the angle and height of the drop. (McD-D)
127. The later FSD airframes and early production models were repainted in camouflage late in 1980 and marked with the tail code of the Hornet test squadron, VX-4, based at NATC Pax River. During a two-week reliability demonstration in December 1980, Hornets proved to be at least three times more trouble-free than either aircraft they are intended to replace. (McD-D)
128. Late in 1980, when the 'bad press' around Hornet reached its peak, McDonnell Douglas and the Navy sponsored a publicity tour of West Coast Naval and Marine Air Stations with a stop at Abbotsford, British Columbia, Canada, by the second production F-18. At MCAS El Toro on 19 August 1980, curious Marines get their first look at what is to be their first-line fighter of the 1980s. (McD-D)

◀126